Dedicated to my son Parker, and my favorite niece and nephew, Logan and Matthew.

Nighty Night Cow.
Mooing and milking
has made her so sleepy.

Nighty Night Donkey.
Hee-hawing and grazing
has him resting so deeply.

Nighty Night Sheepy.
Tired from all of
the baaing and sheering.

Nighty Night Piggy.
Dreaming of oinking as
morning is nearing.

Nighty Night Chicken. Weary from all of the clucking and pecking.

Nighty Night Kitty Cat.
All her meowing had
the old farmer checking.

Nighty Night Ducky.
There will be
plenty of time for
fishing and quacking.

Nighty Night Doggy.
Snoozing and snoring
after woofing and snacking.

Nighty Night Horsey. Worn out from all of the trotting and neighing.

Nighty Night Little Farmer. Tomorrow there will be plenty more playing.

Other titles and book formats from Daniel S. Miller

Nighty Night Car Board Book

Moo Like A Cow! Story & Song Book

Nighty Night Horsey Board Book

Printed in Great Britain
by Amazon